gewidmet.

(Gaelic)

in E moll

für

grosses Orchester

Mrs. H. H. A. Beach.

PARTITUR.

ARTHUR P. SCHMIDT

BOSTON
146 Boylston Street.

LEIPZIG.

NEW YORK
136 Fifth Avenue.

(Facsimile of the Original Title Page)

INSTRUMENTATION

2 Flutes
Piccolo
2 Oboes
English Horn
2 Clarinets in A
Bass Clarinet in A
2 Bassoons

4 Horns in F
2 Trumpets in F
3 Trombones

Timpani
Triangle

Violin I
Violin II
Viola
Violoncello
Bass

Duration: ca. 40 minutes

First performance: October 31, 1896
The Boston Symphony Orchestra
Emil Paur, conductor

ISBN: 1-932419-06-3
ISMN: M-800001-06-2
This score is a slightly modified unabridged reprint of the
score published in 1897 by Arthur P. Schmidt.
The score has been reduced to fit the present format.

Printed in the USA
First Printing: February, 2004

SYMPHONY IN E MINOR
Op. 32
"Gaelic"

Amy Beach (1867-1944)

SERENISSIMA MUSIC, INC.

a 2.
mf
cresc.
p cresc.
p
cresc.
poco a poco
cresc. poco a poco
p cresc.
p
cresc. poco a poco
p
poco a poco crescendo
poco a poco crescendo
poco a poco crescendo
poco a poco crescendo
poco a poco crescendo

poco a poco
a 2.
f
ff
mf
cresc.
a 2.
f
ff
mf
ff
mf
ff
a 2.
ff
f
f
ff
mf
mf
ff
tr
ff
sempre cresc.
ff
sempre cresc.
ff
sempre cresc.
ff
sempre cresc.
ff
sempre cresc.
ff

a 2.
ff
ff
a 2.
ff
a 2.
ff
a 2.
ff
a 2.
ff
ff
tr

tr
più
dim.
più
dim.
tr
più
dim.
tr
più
dim.
f
mf
dim.
p
tr
pp
pizz.
f
mf
sf
pizz.
f
mf
sf
pizz.
f
mf
sf
pizz.
f
mf
sf
pizz.
f
mf
sf

A
A
p
p
p
tr
A
arco
p
pp
arco
p
pp
arco
p
pp
p
dim.
pp
p
dim.
pp

p
p
p
p
tr
p

a 2.
f
mf
mf
a 2.
f
mf
mf
mf
mf
mf
mf
mf
mf
tr
mf
sf
p
cresc.
sf
p
cresc.
sf
p
cresc.
arco
sf
p
cresc.
arco
sf
mf

f
f
cresc.
cresc.
cresc.
f
f
f
tr
f
f
f
f
cresc.
f

B
a 2.
tr
f
a 2.
tr
f
B
a 2.
f
f
f
f
f
B
non legato
sempre f
non legato
sempre f
tr
non legato
sempre f
sempre f
sempre f

rit.
a 2.
ff
tr

a tempo
sf
p
mf
a tempo
ff
ff
p
mf
sf
sf
sf
a tempo
sf
p
mf
sf
mf
p
mf
sf
mf
p
mf
sf
p
mf
sf

a 2.
cresc.

a 2.

f
ff
tr

rall.
p
p
rall.
p
dim.
dim.
dim.
p
pizz.
mf
p

C Poco più tranquillo.
Fag.
Corni.
Timp.
tr
pp
C Poco più tranquillo.
pp
pp
p
pizz.
arco
pp
p
pizz.
arco
pp
p
Fl.
mf
Ob.
mf
I° Solo.
Clar.
mf
espr.
Cor.
p
pizz.
pp
pizz.
pp
pizz.
pp
pp
pp

p espress.
cresc.
f
p
p
p
p
pp
arco
sempre pp
arco
sempre pp
arco
sempre pp
pizz.
arco
pizz.
pizz.
arco
pizz.

D
a 2.
mf
arco

poco rit.
f
ff
mf
poco rit.
p
tr
pizz.
dim.

E
a tempo
Iº Solo.
p
Iº Solo.
p
p
p
E
a tempo
pp
pp
pp
E
a tempo
pizz.
pp
pizz.
pp
pizz.
pp
pizz.
pp
pizz.
pp

p I.
pp
pp
pp
pp
pp
arco
arco
arco
arco
arco
dolce
dolce
dolce
dolce
dolce
pp
pp
pp
pp
pp
dim.
dim.
dim.
dim.

Trb.
rall.
Tempo I.
pp
Tuba.
pp
Timp.
pp
rall.
Tempo I.
sempre pp
sempre pp
sempre pp
sempre pp
dim.
pizz.
Fag.
pp
Cor. I.
1º Solo.
pp
senza cresc.
senza cresc.
senza cresc.
senza cresc.
arco
pp
senza cresc.

p
p
p
p
p
p
pp
pp

rall.
p
a 2.
cresc.
f
mf
pp
poco
a
poco
cresc.

F
a tempo
p
cresc.
p
mf
cresc.
p
mf
cresc.
p
mf
cresc.
F
a tempo
p
p
p
cresc.
p
cresc.
F
a tempo
p
cresc.
p
cresc.
p
cresc.
pizz.
arco
cresc.
pizz.
arco
cresc.

sempre f
sempre f
sempre f
sempre f
sempre f
sempre f
sempre f
sempre f
sempre f
sempre f
sempre f
sempre f
sempre f
sempre f
sempre f

a 2.
sf
sf
f
sf
sf
sf
cresc.
sf
f
p
f
ff
p
sf
sf
div.
p
sf
p
sf
p

G
G
pp
pp
pp
p
Iº
p
pp
G
pizz.
pizz.
unis.
pizz.
pp
pp
pp
pizz.
pp

p
p
p
p
p
p
p
p
p
arco
dolce
arco
dolce
arco
dolce
pizz.
arco
arco

poco cresc.
poco cresc.
poco cresc.
a 2.
p
p
poco cresc.
p
p
poco cresc.
poco cresc.
poco cresc.
poco cresc.
poco cresc.

H
I.
p
p
H
pp
III.
pp
pp
pp
H
pp
pp
pp
pp
pp

p
p
espr.
p
p
p
p
p
espr.
p
p
p
pp
pp
pp
sempre pp
sempre pp
sempre pp
sempre pp
sempre pp

cresc. poco a
poco
cresc. poco a
poco
cresc. poco a
poco
cresc. poco a
cresc. poco a poco
I.
p
pp
cresc. poco a
div.
cresc. poco a
cresc. poco a
cresc. poco a
poco
cresc. poco a
poco
cresc. poco a
poco

più cresc.
mf
poco
unis.

I.
Tr.

I
a 2.
ff
f
tr

sempre ff
sempre ff
sempre ff
a 2.
a 2.
sempre ff
sempre ff
sempre ff
tr
sempre ff
sempre ff
sempre ff
sempre ff
sempre ff
sempre ff

ff
ff
ff
tr
con fuoco
con fuoco
con fuoco

ff
ff
ff
f
f
ff
f
ff
tr
ff

J
sf
J
sf
J
con tutta forza
con tutta forza
con tutta forza
con tutta forza
con tutta forza
sf

dimin.
dimin.
dimin.
dimin.
dimin.
dimin.
dimin.
p
mf
mf
f non legato
f non legato
sfz
sfz
p
p

rall.
G.P.
p
pp
pp
p
pp
rall.
G.P.
pp
rall.
G.P.
p
pp
pp
p
pp
pp
pizz.
pp

Fl.
Più lento.
rall.
Ob.
Clar.
Solo I.
ben espressivo
p
f
p
Fag.
Viol. I.
Più lento.
rall.
pizz.
pp
pizz.
pp
pizz.
pp
pizz.
pp
Tempo I.
p
Tempo I.
pp
arco
pp
arco
pp

I.
p
I.
p
p
I.
pp
pp
pp
pp
pp

K
mf
K
mf
I.
tr
p
K
sf
p
arco
arco

a 2.
f
f
a 2.
f
f
cresc.
f
cresc.
f
f
tr
mf
cresc.
tr
f
cresc.
f
cresc.
f
cresc.
f
cresc.
cresc.
f
mf
cresc.
f

f
f
sempre f
sempre f
sempre f
sempre f
sempre f

a 2.
a 2.

rit.
a tempo.
sf
p
mf
rit.
a tempo.
a 2.
ff
I.
p
mf
a 2.
ff
sf
rit.
a tempo.
sf
p
mf

a 2.

tr
mf
f
p

L
a 2.
L
L

rit.
f
ff
ff
ff
ff
p
rit.
p
ff
ff
ff
ff
ff
ff
rit.
ff
ff
pp
ff
p
ff
ff

Poco più tranquillo.
pp
p.
p
mf I. Solo
pp
pp
Poco più tranquillo.
p
p
Poco più tranquillo.
pp
pizz.
pp
pizz.
pp
pizz.
pizz.
arco
pp
pizz.
pp

p
espress.
cresc.
f
mf
mf
p
arco
sempre pp
arco
sempre pp
arco
sempre pp
pizz.
arco
pizz.
sempre pp
arco
pizz.
sempre pp

M
a 2.
mf
mf
mf
mf
mf
M
mf
M
mf
mf
mf
arco
mf
arco
mf

tr
f
f
tr
f
f
f
f
f
f
f
f
f
f
tr
f
tr
f
f
f
f

ff
p
mf
pp

poco rit.
N a tempo
Solo
p
Solo
p
p
pp
p
poco rit.
N a tempo
I.
p
pp
pp
pp
poco rit.
N a tempo
pizz.
pp
dolce
pizz.
pp
dolce
pizz.
pp
dolce
pizz.
pp
pizz.
pp

tranquillo.
pp
pp
tranquillo.
pp
sempre pp
tranquillo e espressivo.
arco
pp
arco
pp
arco
pp
arco
pp
arco
pp

Fl.
Ob.
Cl.
pp
O
espress.
Cor.
pp
Timp.
dolcissimo
pizz.
arco
pp
calando
pp

Tempo I.
Tempo I.
I.
pp
senza cresc.

pp
pp
pp
cresc.
pp
cresc.
p
cresc.
p
p

P
a 2.
p
mf
f
cresc.
P
cresc.
mf
P
sempre
cresc.
poco
a
poco

Animato.
sempre f
sempre f
sempre f
sempre f
Animato.
più cresc.
f
f
f
f
mf
f
Animato.
f
f
f
f
f

a 2.
sempre f
sempre f
a 2.
sempre f
sempre f
sempre f
f
sempre f
sempre f

Q
a 2.
sf
f
tr

a 2.
a 2.
a 2.
a 2.
tr

a 2.
a 2.
sf
ff
marcato
marcato
tr

marcato
marcato
marcato
ff
ff
ff
ff
ff
ff
ff
ff
ff

con tutta forza
con tutta forza
con tutta forza
con tutta forza
con tutta forza
con tutta forza
con tutta forza
ff
ff
ff
tr
con tutta forza
con tutta forza
con tutta forza
con tutta forza
con tutta forza

R
a 2
sempre ff
a 2
sempre ff
sempre ff
sempre ff
R
sempre ff
sempre ff
sempre ff
sempre ff
sempre ff
sempre ff
tr
R
sempre ff
sempre ff
sempre ff
sempre ff
pesante
sempre ff
pesante

a 2.
a 2.
tr
double corde

II.

Alla Siciliana. (♩. = 40)
Flauto Piccolo.
Flauti.
Oboi.
Clarinetti in B♭
Fagotti.
Corno Inglese.
Alla Siciliana. (♩. = 40)
Corni in F.
Solo
Triangolo.
Timpani F. G. C.
Alla Siciliana. (♩. = 40)
Violini I.
Violini II.
Viole.
Violoncelli.
Contrabassi.

Ob.
Solo
I.
p
Cl.
pp
Fag.
pp
Cor.
pp
pp
pp
pp
pp
pp
Ob.
cresc.
mf
Cl.
cresc.
Fag.
cresc.
Fl.
Ob.
p
Cl.
p
Fag.
p

Fl.
cresc.
f
poco rall.
a tempo
Ob.
dolce
pp
Cl.
Fag.
mf
Cor.
dim.
rall.

Allegro vivace. (♩= 132.)
Ob.
Cl.
Allegro vivace. (♩= 132.)
tr
div. pizz.
sempre pp
pizz.
sempre pp
pizz.
sempre pp
Fl.
mf
Cl.
mf
Cor.
mf
mf
non legato
cresc.
mf
unis. arco
cresc.
mf
cresc.
mf
cresc.
mf
pizz.
cresc.
mf

Fl. picc.
pizz.
pizz.
pizz.
arco
pizz.
arco

A
mf
f
mf
f
mf
f
arco
p staccato
cresc.
pizz.
arco

f
mf
dim.
mf
mf
8
dim.
dim.
dim.
dim.
dim.

1.
3
p
pp
p
p.
p
pp
1.
pizz.
p
pp
pp
pizz.
p
pp
p
pp
p
pp

2.
B
p
3
p
p
p
B
p
pp
2.
B
pp
pp
pp
sempre staccato
arco
p
pp
pp

p
cresc.
mf
sempre staccato
pizz.
arco
pizz.
arco
arco
arco
pp
mf

C
mf
a 2.
f
mf
f
mf
cresc.
f
f
C
f
f
f
f
C
cresc.
cresc.
f con fuoco fp
cresc.
f
p
cresc.
f
fp
cresc.
f
fp
cresc.
f
p

mf
f
f
mf
p
cresc.
p sempre cresc.
poco a poco cresc.
poco a poco cresc.
poco a poco cresc.
sempre cresc.
sempre cresc.

a 2.
dim.
pizz.
pizz.

a 2.
mf
dim.
dim.
dim.
p
mf
p
dim.
pp
pizz.
p
più dim.
pizz.
p
più dim.
p
dim.
p
più dim.
p
più dim.

D
I.
I.
p
p
D
I. Solo
p
espressivo
pp
D
pp
pp
pp
arco
pp
arco
pp

I.
mf
I. Solo
mf
ben espressivo
a 2.
mf
a 2.
mf
mf
cantabile
arco
pp
sempre staccato
cantabile
pp
arco

a 2.
mf
Corno Inglese.
Solo.
mf
mf
mf
mf
mf
mf

a 2
mf
I.
mf
mf
I.
mf
mf
espressivo
mf
mf
mf
p
cresc.
p
cresc.
p
cresc.
pizz.
p
arco
cresc.

E
II.
a 2.
E
E
pizz.
pizz.

f
cresc.
cresc.
cresc.
cresc.
cresc.
ff
ff
ff
ff
ff
ff
cresc.
cresc.
ff
ff
cresc.
ff
cresc.
ff
con fuoco
cresc.
ff
con fuoco
cresc.
ff
arco
cresc.
ff
arco
cresc.
ff

dim.
dim.
dim.
dim.
dim.
p
dim.
dim.
mf
p
dim.
dim.
mf
p
dim.
dim.
sempre dim.
dim.
dim.
sempre dim.
p
pizz.
arco
dim.
sempre dim.
p
pizz.
dim.
sempre dim.
p
pizz.
dim.
sempre dim.
p

I.
più dim.
I.
p
pp
ppp

Fl.
F
a 2.
p
Ob.
pp
Clar.
pp
Fag.
tr
pp
F
Cor.
pp
F
pizz.
pp
div.
pizz.
pp
pizz.
pp
arco
tr
pp
cresc.
tr
pizz.
pp

poco a poco più animato
cresc.
mf
p
cresc.
tr
arco
pizz.

a 2.
cresc.
f
a 2.
cresc.
f
a 2.
cresc.
f
mf cresc.
f
cresc.
f
a 2.
mf cresc.
f
f
f
f
f
tr
f
tr
f
f
f

Fl. piccolo
Tempo I.
a 2.
a 2.
I. Solo.
p espr.
Tempo I.
I. Solo.
p espr.
Tempo I.
divisi
con sordini
pp
divisi
con sordini
pp
div. pizz.
pp
div. pizz.
pp

Fl.
p
Ob.
mf
Corno Inglese.
Solo
p
espr.
8
sempre div. e ppp
sempre div. e ppp
sempre div. e pp
sempre div. e pp
pizz.
pp

Solo
p
p
pp
p
p
cresc.
mf
dim.
pp
tr
pp
unis.
senza cresc.
unis.
senza cresc.
unis.
arco
pp
unis.
sempre pp
sempre pp

G
a 2.
mf
cresc.
a 2
pp
G
senza sordini
pizz.
p
cresc.

I.
mf
cresc.
mf
cresc.
mf
p
arco
p
cresc.
arco
p
cresc.
arco
p
cresc.
arco
p
cresc.
arco
p
cresc.

a 2.
mf
f
a 2.
f
a 2.
f
Soli
ff ben espressivo
f
f
mf
f
mf
f
tr
mf
cresc.
sf
più cresc.
f
pizz.
sf
dim.
p
pizz.
più cresc.
f
sf
dim.
p
pizz.
più cresc.
f
sf
dim.
p
pizz.
più cresc.
f
p
dim.
p
pizz.
più cresc.
f
p
dim.
p

rall.
Solo
mf espr.
sempre dim.
pp
Solo
mf
sempre dim.
pp
rall.
pp
rall.
arco
tr
pp
tr
arco
pp
arco
tr
pp
pp
pp
pp

Allegro vivace.
pp
pp
pp
pp
pp
sempre pp
Allegro vivace.
non legato
sempre pp
non legato
sempre pp
pizz.
sempre pp
arco
sempre pp
sempre pp

Fl picc.
pp
I.
pp
a 2.
pp
I.
pp
III.
Triang.
pp
Timp.
sempre pp
sempre pp
sempre pp
sempre pp
sempre pp

pp
pp
pp
pp
pp
pp
pp
pp
pizz.
pizz.
pizz.
div.
div.
pp
pp
pp
pp
pp

III.

Lento con molto espressione. (♩ = 72.)
Flauti.
Oboi.
Clarinetti in A.
Bass Clarinetto in A.
Fagotti.
Corni in F.
Trombe in F.
Tromboni e Tuba.
Timpani in B u. E.
Lento con molto espressione. (♩ = 72.)
Violini I.
Violini II.
Viole.
Violoncelli.
Contrabassi.
espr.
mf espr.
pizz.
dim.

Fl.
espr.
mf
p
Ob.
I.
Cl.
p
Bass Cl.
pp
pp
Cor.
p
pp
p
pp
Trombe.
p
p
Timp.
pp
Viol. Solo.
mf
Vcll.
p
dim.
Cb.
p
dim.
Cl.
B. Cl.
Timp.
p
Viol. Solo.
quasi recitativo
accel.
sost.
con strepito
ff
p con sordini
ff
non legato
Viol.
con sordini
Viola.
con sordini
Cb.

Viol. Solo
rit.molto a tempo
A
con tutta forza
sf
dim.
mf
p
Viol.
pizz.
arco
mf
p
pp
Viola
Vcll. Solo.
ben espress.
Vcll.
Cb.
sempre pp
cresc.

Fl.
Ob.
I.
p cantabile
mf
Cl.
p
mf
Bass Cl.
Fag.
p
mf
Cor.
mf
Trombe.
Timp.
Viol. Solo.
f
dim.
p
Viol.
p
pp
Viola.
p
pp
Vcll. Solo
f
p
Vcll.
div.
pizz.
arco
p
dim.
pp
Cb.
arco
p

cresc.
I.
f
cresc.
mf
mf
mf
cresc.
p
mf cresc.
I.
mf cresc.
ff
cresc.
pizz.
arco
pizz.
arco

tr
mf
p
tr
mf
sempre dim. e espr.
p
dim.
p
dim.
p
dim.
mf
ben
pizz.
arco
p
pizz.
p

Più mosso. (♩ = 84.)

rit.

Fl.

f

Ob.

f

Cl.

f

Bass Cl.

f

Fag.

f

rit.

Più mosso. (♩ = 84.)

f

Cor.

f

Trombe.

a 2.

f

Tromboni

f

e Tuba.

f

Timp.

pp

f

rit.

Più mosso. (♩ = 84.)

pp

f

senza sordini

pp *ppp*

f

senza sordini

f

senza sordini

pp

f

espress. *p*

f

pizz.

dim. *pp*

f

pizz.

dim. *pp*

f

pizz.

mf
a 2.
cresc.
a 2.
a 2.
arco
arco
cresc. molto

B
ff
B
ff
B
ff

a 2
a 2

a 2
a 2.
a 2.
pesante
pesante

C
sf
dim.
cantabile
mf
p cantabile
f
mf
p

mf
mf
mf
mf
mf
mf
12
6
cresc.
cresc.
cresc.
cresc.
cresc.

rit.
f
ff
p
sf
rit.
pp
rit.
pizz
arco
pizz
arco

Tempo I.
mf
mf
cantab.
p
cantab.
p
mf
Tempo I.
p
p
Tempo I.
dolce cantabile
dolce
dolce
marcato ma piano
marcato ma piano

mf
cresc.
mf
mf
dim.
p
mf
dim.
p
mf
dim.
p
mf
dim.
p
mf
dim.
mf
pp
pizz.
pp
cresc.
p
dim.
arco
pp
pizz.
pp
cresc.
p
dim.
arco
pp
pizz.
pp
cresc.
p
dim.
arco
pp
pizz.
pp
cresc.
p
dim.
arco
pp
pizz.
pp
cresc.
p
dim.
arco
pp

D
mf
mf
mf
mf
mf
mf
D
mf
D
dolce
mf
dolce
mf
dolce
mf
dolce
mf
mf
mf

a 2.
mf
cresc.
tr
f
cresc.
mf
espressivo
dim.
p
dim.
cresc.
dim.
mf espressivo
pizz.

sempre dim.
sempre dim.
I.
p
p
pp
sempre
pp
più dim.
sempre dim.
più dim.
sempre dim.
più dim.
sempre dim.
sempre dim.
arco
p
sempre dim.

E
p
p
mf cantabile
pp
E
pp
pp
tr
pp
E
pp
pp
pp
pp
pizz.
pp
pizz.

agitato
agitato
agitato
agitato
mf
mf
p
cresc.
cresc.
cresc.
I.
mf
agitato
I.
p
cresc.
I.
mf
agitato
Viol. Solo.
agitato
mf
f
agitato
agitato

rit.
Cor I.II.
rit.
Trombe
Viol.
Solo.
accel.
non legato
rit.
a tempo
rit.
Viola.
rit.
Celli e C. Bassi.
arco
Cl.
Bass Cl.
rit.
Viol. Solo col Viol. I.
rit.
pp dolcissimo
espr.
pp dolcissimo
espr.
dolcissimo
espr.

a tempo
F
Fl.
p dolce cantabile
Ob.
I.
pp
Cl.
pp
Bass Cl.
pp
mf
Fag.
p
Cor. I.II.
pp
p
rit.
a tempo
p
p
I.
p
p
p
p
rit.
a tempo
p
pp
2 Viol.Soli.
rit.
a tempo
mf
f
dim.
a tempo
rit.
p
mf
dim.
pp
p
mf
dim.
pp
p
mf
dim.
pp
pizz.
p
mf
dim.
pp
pizz.
p
dim.

poco rall.
a tempo
G (♩= 72)
a 2.
mf
3
a 2.
mf
a 2.
mf
poco rall.
a tempo
G
mf
mf
mf
mf
poco rall.
a tempo
G (♩= 72)
3
pp
poco rall.
a tempo
(♩= 72)
3
mf
mf
mf
arco
f
arco
pp
f

f
f
f
f
f
f
f
f
f
f

a 2.
sf
I Solo.
mf
cantabile
mf
p
pp
p
IV.
pp
pp
pp
pp
p
p
pp

H
a 2.
mf
sempre cresc.
ff
espr.
1.
p
dim.

cresc. molto
cresc. molto
cresc. molto
cresc. molto
a 2.
cresc. molto
a 2.
cresc. molto
cresc. molto
cresc. molto
cresc. molto
cresc. molto
cresc. molto
cresc. molto
cresc. molto
cresc. molto
cresc. molto
cresc. molto

a 2.
fff
dim.
mf
f
poco a poco dim.
tr

rall.
f
p dolce
sf
rall.
p
tr
rall.
mf
pizz.

I (♩= 66)
Basscl.
con molto espressione
rall.
I (♩= 66)
rall.
pp
pp
pp
arco
p espr.
pp
pp
Più tranquillo.
Clar. I.
p
Più tranquillo.
sostenuto
dolcissimo
sostenuto
dolcissimo
sostenuto
dolcissimo
sostenuto
dolcissimo
arco
sostenuto
pp

p
pp
mf
Violino Solo.
Violoncello Solo.
mf espressivo

rit.
sempre rit.
Molto Adagio.
lunga
rit.
sempre rit.
Molto Adagio.
lunga
rit.
sempre rit.
Molto Adagio.
lunga

IV.

Allegro di molto. (𝅗𝅥 = 132.)
Flauti.
Oboi.
Clarinetti in A.
Fagotti.
Corni in F.
Trombe in F.
Tromboni
e
Tuba.
Timpani in F♯, B und E.
Violini I.
Violini II.
Viole.
Violoncelli.
Contrabassi.
a 2.
ff
tr

Ob.
Clar.
Fag.
Cor.
Tromboni
Viol. I.
sf
pp
senza cresc.
sf pp
senza cresc.
sf pp
senza cresc.
sf
pp
senza cresc.
sf
pp
senza cresc.
Viol. I.
Viol. II.
Viola
Celli
Bassi

A
p
cresc.
3
p
p
cresc.
p
cresc.
3
A
cresc.
p
3
p
cresc.
3
tr
p
A
poco cresc.
poco cresc.
poco cresc.
poco cresc.
poco cresc.

a 2.

a 2.
mf
cresc.
f
più cresc.

a 2.
a 2.
a 2.

ff
tr
a 2.
non legato

sempre f
sempre f
sempre f
sempre f
sempre
f
sempre
f
sempre
f

B
a 2.
a 2.
B
B

a 2.
f
dim.
f
a 2.
a 2.
f dim.
dim.
ff
dim.
dim.
dim.
dim.
dim.

Solo.
espr.
Solo.
sempre
dim.
pp

a 2.
p
mf
f
pp
p
p
cresc.
mf
mf
f
mf
p
mf
cresc.
cresc.
mf
cresc.
cresc.
cresc.

C
mf
cresc.
cresc.
f
f
f
f
C
cresc.
cresc.
f
f
f
C
f
f
f
f
f

ff
sf
f
tr

rall.
p
pp
a 2.
p cantabile
rall.
p
pp
p
pp
dim.
p
pp
dim.
p
pp
dim.
p
pp
rall.
dim.
p
pp
dim.
p
pp
dim.
p
p cantabile
p cantabile
dim.
dim.
mf
p

Poco più lento. (𝅗𝅥 = 100)
p
a 2
dolce
p
espr.
mf
Poco più lento. (𝅗𝅥 = 100)
p
p
mf
p
Poco più lento. (𝅗𝅥 = 100)
dolce
cresc.
dolce
cresc.
espr.
mf
espr.
mf
pizz.
arco
pp
poco cresc.
mf

a 2.
mf
mf
f
dim.
mf
f
mf
f
ff
dim.
ben es-
dim.
p
pp
poco a poco
mf
dim.
cresc.
f
dim.

D
a 2.
pp
f
mf
f
pressivo
pp
f
D
pp
mf
pp
pp
mf
p espr.
mf
pp
pp
pp
D
pp
ben espressivo
pp
pp
ben espressivo
pp
pp
pp
pp
marcato
pp
marcato

a 2.
a 2.
dim.
dim.
f
f
f
dim.
dim.
I.
f
mf
mf
f
dim.
mf
f
dim.
f
dim.
f
dim.
f
dim.
f
dim.
f
dim.

p
mf
p
pp espr.
pp
mf
dim.
pp
più dim.
p
pp
più dim.
p
sempre espr.
pp
pizz.

rit.
Tempo I. (𝅗𝅥 = 132)
f
f
f
f
rit.
Tempo I. (𝅗𝅥 = 132)
f
f
f
a 2.
f con vigore
a 2.
f con vigore
f
rit.
Tempo I. (𝅗𝅥 = 132)
f
f
f
arco
f
arco
f

a 2.
ff
ff
ff
ff
cresc.
ff
cresc.
ff
ff
ff
ff
mf
cresc.
non legato
ff
mf
cresc.
non legato
ff
mf
cresc.
ff
ff
ff

E
a 2.
sempre f
sempre f
sempre f
sempre f
E
sempre f
sempre f
sempre f
f
E
sempre f
sempre f
ff
sempre f
sempre f

a 2.
tr
ff
cresc.
f

a 2.
tr
tr
tr
pizz.
pizz.
arco
arco

a 2
f
sf
tr
non legato
non legato
non legato

F
Solo.
F
F

p
pp
pp
p
p
pp
pp
poco a poco
poco a poco cresc.
poco a poco cresc.

p
p
p
pp
p
p
pp
pp
pp
poco
cresc.
cresc.
p
poco a poco

p
mf
p
p
mf
p
mf
pp
pp
pp
p espr.
cresc.
p espr.
p
p
p

p
cresc.
mf
mf espr.
p
p
p
mf espr.
p
pp
p
pp
tr
p
mf
mf
mf
marcato
mf espr.
marcato
mf

G
mf
mf
G
mf
mf
G
cresc.
cresc.
cresc.
cresc.
cresc.

mf cresc.
f
cresc.
mf cresc.
f
cresc.
f
f
cresc.
f
cresc.
mf
cresc.
mf
mf
più cresc.
f
più cresc.
f
più cresc.
f
più cresc.
f
più cresc.
f

a 2.
sempre cresc.
f
a 2.
sempre cresc.
f
f
f
sempre cresc.
sempre cresc.
sempre cresc.

H
ff
H
ff
tr
ff
H
ff

a 2.
a 2.
a 2.
ff
tr
ff
tr

I
I
p
sf p
p
sf p
sf dim.
mf
p
dim. molto
pp
I
dim. molto
p
pp
dim. molto
p
pp
dim. molto
p
pp
dim. molto
p
pp
dim. molto
p
pp

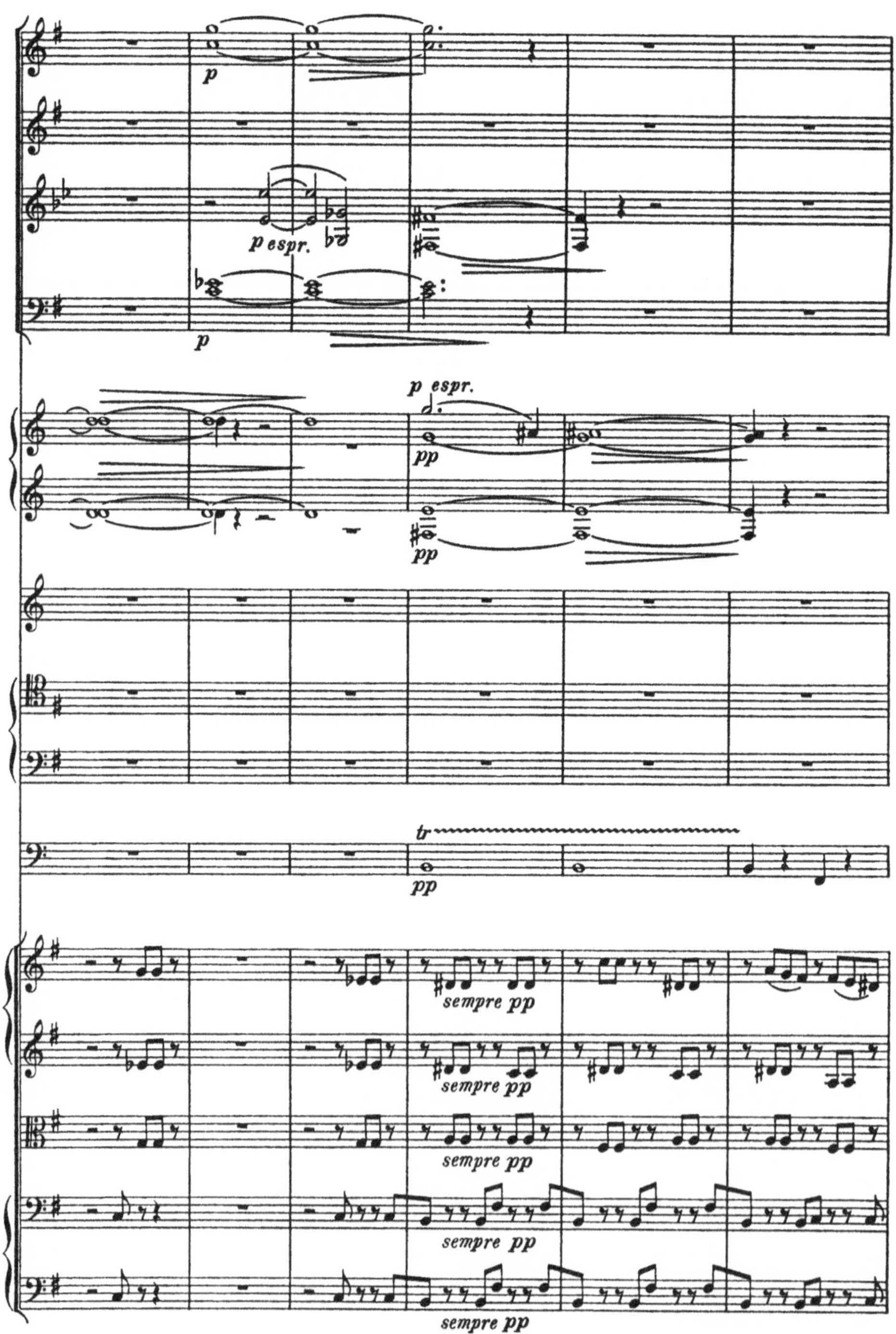
p
p espr.
p
p espr.
pp
pp
tr
pp
sempre pp
sempre pp
sempre pp
sempre pp
sempre pp

K
p
p
p
K
K

a 2.
p
p
mf
p
mf
p
mf
p
tr
pp
cresc.
p
poco cresc.
p
poco cresc.
p
poco cresc.
p
poco cresc.
p
poco cresc.
p

a 2.
mf
cresc.
mf
cresc.
mf
cresc.
mf cresc.
cresc.
a 2.
mf
mf
più cresc.
mf
cresc.
cresc.
cresc.
cresc.
cresc.

a 2.

a 2.
a 2.
ff
tr
ff non legato
ff non legato
non legato

L
a 2.
L
a 2.
a 2.
tr
L

sempre ff
sempre f
sempre f
sempre f
f
f
sempre f
sempre f
divisi
sempre f
sempre f
sempre f

rall.
mf
p
mf marcato
p
mf
mf
rall.
p
p
p
p
p
3
rall.
f dim.
p
pp dol.
f dim.
p
pp dol.
f dim.
sempre dim.
p
più dim.
pp
pizz.
mf
sempre dim.
pizz.
mf
sempre dim.

(𝅗𝅥 = 100)
pp
poco cresc.
p
poco cresc.
pp
poco cresc.
p
poco cresc.
(𝅗𝅥 = 100)
pp
p
pp
pp
p
p
(𝅗𝅥 = 100)
ce cantabile
poco a poco cresc.
ce cantabile
poco a poco cresc.
poco a poco cresc.
pp
p
poco a poco cresc.
pp
poco a poco cresc.

a2.
mf
mf
dim.
cresc.
cresc.
f
dim.

M
p
pp
pp
pp
pp
p marcato
M
p ben espressivo
III.
dim.
pp
IV.
espr.
pp
pp
pp
M
p
pp
p
pp
pp
pp
unis.
espr.
espr.
arco
p espr.
pp
arco
pp
p marcato

a 2.
mf
f
dim.
a 2.
cresc. molto
tr
p

p espr.
p
espr.
p
p espr.
p
pp
dim.
pp
p
espr.
pp
pp
tr
pp
più dim.
pp
più dim.
pp
più dim.
pp
pizz.
pp
pizz.
pp

N
N
tr
pp
N
dolce
sul tasto
dolce
sul tasto
dolce
sul tasto
arco
sempre pp
arco
sempre pp

poco a poco rall.
Tempo I.
I Solo.
p
con molto espressione
pp
poco a poco rall.
Tempo I.
pp
tr
pp
tr
pp
poco a poco rall.
Tempo I.
ben tranquillo
pp
ben tranquillo
pp
ben tranquillo
pp marc.
ben tranquillo
pp marc.

pp
p
p
p
pp
p
p
tr
pp
poco
cresc.
cresc.
sf
p
cresc.
sf
poco
cresc.
poco
cresc.

a 2.
mf
poco a poco cresc.
mf
poco a poco cresc.
mf
poco a poco cresc.
poco a poco cresc.
mf
p
poco a poco
p
p
p
p
tr
cresc. poco a poco
mf
poco a poco cresc.
sf
poco a poco cresc.
sf
poco a poco cresc.
poco a poco cresc.
poco a poco cresc.

O
sf
mf
sf
p
cresc.
sf
mf
a 2.
mf
O
mf
poco a poco
cresc.
mf
poco a poco cresc.
sf
cresc.
sf
poco a poco cresc.
sf
poco a poco cresc.
sf
sf
O
p
sempre cresc.
sf
p
sempre cresc.
sf
mf marcato
p
sempre
p
sempre

a 2.
cresc.
mf
cresc.
cresc.
a 2.
cresc.
cresc.
cresc.
mf
a 2.
mf
cresc.
a 2.
mf
cresc.
mf
mf
non legato
non legato
sempre
cresc.
non legato
cresc.
non legato
cresc.
non legato

a 2.
f
più cresc.
più cresc.
f
f
f
più cresc.
f
più cresc.
f
f
cresc.
f
cresc.
f
cresc.
f marcato
f
sempre cresc.
f
sempre cresc.
f
sempre cresc.
f
sempre cresc.
f
sempre cresc.

a 2
ff

a 2.
ff
ff
ff
ff
ff
ff
sf
sf
sf
sf
sf

P
a 2.
mf
mf
mf
p
P
mf
ff
p
ff
tr
ff
pp
poco
a
poco
cresc.
P
sf
ff
sf p
poco
a
poco
sf
ff
sf p
poco
a
poco
sf
ff
sf p
poco
a
poco
sf
sf
p
poco
a
poco
cresc.
sf
sf
p
poco
a
poco
cresc.

mf
mf
f
cresc.
p
cresc.
f
tr
f
cresc.
più cresc.
cresc.
più cresc.
cresc.
più cresc.
più cresc.
più cresc.

ff
ff
ff
ff
ff
ff
ff
tr
ff
ff
ff
ff
ff

rit.
ff
ff
ff
rit.
ff
ff
ff
ff
rit.
con gran forza
con gran forza
con gran forza
con gran forza
sf
con gran forza

Ritmo di tre battute. (𝅗𝅥 = 100)
a 2.
ff molto marcato
a 2.
ff
ff
ff
Ritmo di tre battute. (𝅗𝅥 = 100)
f
mf
f
mf
a 2.
molto marcato
f
mf
f
mf
sempre f
Ritmo di tre battute. (𝅗𝅥 = 100)
sempre molto tenuto e
ff
sempre molto tenuto e
ff
sempre molto tenuto e
ff
sempre molto tenuto e
ff
sempre ff

a 2.
sempre ff
sempre ff
sempre ff
mf
mf
sempre ff
mf
mf
mf
cresc.
sempre ff
sempre ff
sempre ff
sempre ff
sempre ff

Ritmo di due battute.
poco a
a 2.
poco a
a 2.
sempre ff
poco a
Ritmo di due battute.
f
poco a
f
crescendo
f
poco a
f
poco a
Ritmo di due battute.
con passione e
poco a
con passione e
poco a
con passione e
poco a
con passione e
poco a
con passione e
poco a

Tempo I.
poco accel.
fff
poco accel.
fff
poco accel.
fff
Tempo I.
poco accel.
fff
fff
a 2.
fff
poco accel.
poco accel.
fff
Tempo I.
poco accel.
fff
poco accel.
fff
poco accel.
fff
poco accel.
fff
poco accel.
fff

a 2.
Q
sempre con tutta forza
sempre con tutta forza
sempre con tutta forza
Q
sempre con tutta forza
sempre con tutta forza
sempre fff
tr
tr
energico
Q
mf non legato cresc.
energico
mf non legato cresc.
sempre ff
sempre con tutta forza
sempre con tutta forza

sempre cresc.
sempre cresc.

a 2.
a 2.
a 2.
a 2.
ff
ff
ff
ff
ff
tr

R
a 2.
fff
R
fff
II.
marcato
3
R

marcato
marcato
non legato
non legato
non legato

sempre fff
sempre fff
sempre fff
sempre fff
sempre fff
sempre fff
sempre fff
sempre fff
sempre fff
tr
sempre ff
tr
sempre fff
sempre fff
sempre fff
sempre fff
sempre fff

CPSIA information can be obtained
at www.ICGtesting.com
Printed in the USA
LVHW111253081019
633551LV00001B/20/P

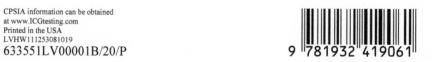

9 781932 419061